WILD THE SWANS

Illustrated by Pam Storey
Story re-told by Grace De La Touche

© 1993 Grandreams Limited

Published by
Grandreams Limited
Jadwin House, 205/211 Kentish Town Road, London, NW5 2JU.

Printed in Italy

GS13-16

Long ago and far away there lived a King. He was very proud of his eleven sons and one daughter. All of his children were good, kind and wise, even young Eliza who was still only a baby.

The Queen had sadly died and after a while, feeling that his children needed a mother, the King married again.

His new Queen was very jealous of the eleven princes and Eliza, and life for them soon changed. Eliza was sent to the country to be brought up on a farm.

The Queen turned the King from his sons, by telling lies to him about them. Soon the King cared nothing for his sons. The Queen was delighted.

"Go, you big ugly birds," she cried to them one day, casting a spell on them. But the worst she could do was to turn them into swans with golden crowns on their heads. Away they flew.

They flew over the cottage where Eliza lived, but no-one saw them.

Eliza lived happily at the farm, but she missed her brothers. When she was fifteen, she returned to the palace.

The Queen was furious at how pretty Eliza had become, and would dearly have liked to turn her into a swan like her brothers.

Instead she bathed Eliza and put three toads in to change her looks. The toads were instantly turned to poppies by Eliza's innocence and goodness.

The Queen then used walnut juice to darken Eliza's skin, and matted her hair with fat.

"This will make the King reject you," said the Queen, and the King did turn from Eliza. He did not know that this messy girl brought before him was his daughter.

Eliza was very upset and decided to run away to look for her brothers. She went over the fields and through the forests. She came at last to a stream and saw her own reflection.

"No wonder my father did not know me," she said, and she jumped in to wash herself. Moments later the real Eliza emerged, with clean golden hair and fair skin.

For many days she walked, looking for her brothers. One day she met an old woman. She had a basket of fruit and shared some with Eliza.

"Have you seen eleven princes riding through the forest?" asked Eliza.

"I haven't, my dear," said the old woman. "But yesterday I did see eleven swans riding down the stream. Each had a golden crown on his head." She showed Eliza the river .

Eliza followed the river to the shore, and stood watching the waves. As the sun was setting, eleven swans flew down to the shore. As the sun set, the swans turned into eleven princes with golden crowns on their heads.

"My brothers!" cried Eliza, and she ran to greet them. They were delighted to see their young sister, now grown into a lovely girl. They soon realised that it was because of the wicked Queen that they were rejected.

"We are swans during the day," said the eldest. "But when the sun goes down, we regain our human form. We therefore have to be over land when the sun sets or we will be doomed."

"We will take you with us when we leave tomorrow," said the youngest. "Tonight we must weave a net to carry you."

All night the brothers and sister wove a net. In the morning as Eliza slept, eleven swans flew up into the air, carrying the net. The youngest shaded Eliza's face from the sun with his wing.

On the other side of the sea was a beautiful land. The brothers flew hard to reach it in daylight.

"Here is your new home," they said as they landed.

Eliza had a dream that night. A fairy came to her and said, "There is a way to save your brothers, but it means hardship and pain for you. There are stinging nettles around the cave. Gather them, although they will sting, and trample them with your feet. With the flax, weave and make up eleven mail shirts for your brothers. But you must never speak, from the moment you start until you finish, even if it takes years, or your brothers will die."

Eliza awoke with a nettle stinging her hand.

Her brothers had already left as it was broad daylight, so Eliza began her work. When they returned and saw her poor blistered hands, and she would not say a word, they realised that she was working for them. Two more days and the first shirt was finished. A day later, she was at her work, when the royal huntsmen came to the forest. She ran to her cave in fright, but the dogs followed her. The King was amongst the huntsmen and fell in love with Eliza when he saw her.

"I'll take you to the palace, where you may make your home," he told Eliza.

Eliza was beautifully dressed, and the King chose to make her his Queen, but she would not smile or say a word.

"My present to you," he said, taking her to a small chamber, "is a room like your cave, with all your familiar things around you."

There Eliza saw the prepared nettles and the completed shirt and she was happy.

Night after night the young Queen crept away from the King to continue her work.

Soon seven shirts were completed, but she had no more flax. Eliza knew that the nearest nettles grew in the graveyard.

At the dead of night, while all were asleep, she crept out to the graveyard. On a gravestone sat seven witches, counting the dead. Eliza walked straight past, with a shudder.

The Archbishop was the only one to have seen Eliza leave, and he had followed her. He did not trust her, and thought she had bewitched the King.

"The Queen is a witch," the Archbishop told the King. "I have proof."

The King did not want to believe it, but he watched when Eliza went out at night. Night after night, she continued her weaving in the small room. Then one night, with one shirt to go, Eliza ran out of flax and nettles. She would have to visit the graveyard again. This time the King followed. He saw the witches on the gravestone and believed Eliza to be one of them.

"The people must judge her," said the King sadly.
And the people judged that she was a witch and should be
burned at the stake.

Eliza was thrown into prison. Her pillows and
sheets were the nettle shirts. She could not have wished
for better blankets, and she continued her work.

Eleven princes arrived that night at the palace gate,
demanding to see the King.

"It's too late to disturb the King," said the guards.
Eleven swans flew off as dawn broke.

Eliza was carried to the stake in a cart, still sewing and weaving the eleventh shirt. The others lay at her feet.

"Look at the witch!" cried the mob. "She still sews! She's casting spells. Take it from her!"

The people were about to tear the shirts from her when eleven swans appeared, golden crowns on their heads, flapping their wings and forcing the people back.

The executioner went to tie Eliza to the stake, but Eliza quickly threw the shirts over her brothers, and they became princes again. Sadly the youngest still had a wing instead of an arm, as Eliza had not quite finished the shirt.

"Now I may speak!" cried Eliza, turning to the King.

The whole story was told to the King, who was very happy. He did not want to loose Eliza.

As the eldest prince spoke, the wood at the stake blossomed and a huge rose bush sprang up.